Washington Irving

RIP VAN WINKLE

adapted by
Jeffrey Busch

ARTIST

Willie Schubert

LETTERER

BERKLEY/FIRST PUBLISHING

For Washington Irving, the world was a fertile field from which an astute and observant traveller could reap an abundant harvest of ideas. Irving's most popular works resulted from the research and observations he gathered while carefully noting the goings-on around him. The premises of both **Rip Van Winkle** and *The Legend of Sleepy Hollow,* for example, were old European folk tales that had passed orally from generation to generation long before Irving was exposed to them during his rambling travels. Irving's versions, though, were not simply transcribed and transposed to his native America; his tales were humorous, graceful, and thoughtfully constructed. Collected with *The Legend of Sleepy Hollow* and a number of essays on English life, **Rip Van Winkle** was published in 1820 in *The Sketch Book,* which was credited to "Geoffrey Crayon," one of Irving's pseudonyms. Irving had already distinguished himself as an American literary figure with *Letters of Jonathon Oldstyle, Gent.,* a satirical series on New York society, and *History of New York,* a rollicking burlesque attributed to Diedrich Knickerbocker, an imaginary Dutch-American scholar. But it was *The Sketch Book,* his most successful work, that elicited the friendly attention of such literary luminaries as Sir Walter Scott and Lord Byron, and won Irving international fame — the first ever accorded an American writer. Irving's next book, *Bracebridge Hall* (1822), another collection of sketches, was well received, but he was discouraged by harsh criticism of *Tales of a Traveller* (1824) and briefly gave up writing. Irving eventually recovered and went on to regain success and fame with several other collections of sketches, a number of exhaustive biographies and several painstaking historical studies. Although his later efforts lacked the focus, wit, and grace of his earlier works, at his death in 1859 Irving was widely recognized as a leading American writer.

Rip Van Winkle
Classics Illustrated, Number 11

Wade Roberts, Editorial Director
Alex Wald, Art Director
Mike McCormick, Production Manager

PRINTING HISTORY
1st edition published July 1990

For information, address: First Publishing, Inc., 435 North LaSalle St., Chicago, Illinois 60610.

ISBN 0-425-12258-1

Distributed by Berkley Sales & Marketing, a division of The Berkley Publishing Group, 200 Madison Avenue, New York, New York 10016.

Printed in the United States of America

1 2 3 4 5 6 7 8 9 0

Whoever has made a voyage up the Hudson must remember the Kaatskill Mountains. They are a dismembered branch of the great Appalachian family, and are seen away to the west of the river, swelling up to a noble height and lording it over the surrounding country. Every change of season, every change of weather, indeed, every hour of the day, produces some change in the magical hues and shapes of these mountains, and they are regarded by all the good wives, far and near, as perfect barometers.

When the weather is fair and settled, they are clothed in blue and purple and print their bold outlines on the clear evening sky.

But, sometimes, when the rest of the landscape is cloudless, they will gather a hood of gray vapors about their summits, which, in the last rays of the setting sun, will glow and light up like a crown of glory.

AT THE FOOT OF THESE FAIRY MOUNTAINS THE VOYAGER MAY HAVE DESCRIBED THE LIGHT SMOKE CURLING UP FROM A LITTLE VILLAGE OF GREAT ANTIQUITY, HAVING BEEN FOUNDED BY SOME OF THE DUTCH COLONISTS IN THE EARLY TIMES OF THE PROVINCE.

IN THAT SAME VILLAGE, WHILE THE COUNTRY WAS YET A PROVINCE OF GREAT BRITAIN...

...THERE LIVED IN ONE OF THESE VERY HOUSES...

...A SIMPLE, GOOD-NATURED FELLOW, OF THE NAME OF RIP VAN WINKLE.

He was a simple, good-natured man...

...a kind neighbor...

...and an obedient, henpecked husband.

Indeed, the latter might account for the meekness of spirit that gained him such universal popularity...for those men are most apt to be easy-going and agreeable abroad who are under the discipline of shrews at home.

Their tempers are rendered pliant and malleable in the fiery furnace of domestic tribulation, and a curtain lecture is worth all the sermons in the world for teaching the virtues of patience and long-suffering. A nagging wife may, therefore in some respects, be considered a blessing. If so, Rip Van Winkle was thrice blessed.

He would carry a fowling piece on his shoulder for hours together, trudging through woods and swamps, up hill and down dale, to shoot a few squirrels or wild pigeons.

The great error in Rip's composition was an insuperable aversion to all kinds of profitable labor. It could not be from want or diligence of perseverance--for he would sit on a wet rock, with a rod as long as a Tartar's lance, and fish all day without a murmur, even though he should not be encouraged by a single nibble.

HE WOULD NEVER REFUSE TO ASSIST A NEIGHBOR IN EVEN THE ROUGHEST TOIL AND WAS A FOREMOST MAN AT ALL COUNTRY FROLICS FOR HUSKING INDIAN CORN OR BUILDING STONE FENCES.

THE WOMEN OF THE VILLAGE, TOO, USED TO EMPLOY HIM TO RUN THEIR ERRANDS AND TO DO SUCH LITTLE ODD JOBS AS THEIR LESS OBLIGING HUSBANDS WOULD NOT DO FOR THEM.

IN A WORD, RIP WAS READY TO ATTEND TO ANYBODY'S BUSINESS BUT HIS OWN, BUT AS TO FAMILY DUTY, AND KEEPING HIS FARM IN ORDER, HE FOUND IT IMPOSSIBLE.

IN FACT, HE DECLARED IT WAS OF NO USE TO WORK ON HIS FARM.

IT WAS THE MOST PESTILENT LITTLE PIECE OF GROUND IN THE WHOLE COUNTRY. EVERYTHING ABOUT IT WENT WRONG, AND WOULD GO WRONG, IN SPITE OF HIM.

HIS CHILDREN, TOO, WERE AS RAGGED AND WILD AS IF THEY BELONGED TO NOBODY. HIS SON, RIP, AN URCHIN BEGOTTEN IN HIS OWN LIKENESS, PROMISED TO INHERIT THE HABITS, WITH THE OLD CLOTHES, OF HIS FATHER.

RIP VAN WINKLE, HOWEVER, WAS ONE OF THOSE HAPPY MORTALS, OF FOOLISH, WELL-OILED DISPOSITIONS, WHO TAKE THE WORLD EASY, AND WOULD RATHER STARVE ON A PENNY THAN WORK FOR A POUND.

IF LEFT TO HIMSELF, HE WOULD HAVE WHISTLED LIFE AWAY IN PERFECT CONTENTMENT.

But his wife kept continually dinning in his ears about his idleness...

...his carelessness...

...and the ruin he was bringing on the family...

Morning, noon and night, her tongue was incessantly going, and everything he said or did was sure to produce a torrent of household eloquence.

RIP'S SOLE DOMESTIC ADHERENT WAS HIS DOG, WOLF, WHO WAS AS MUCH HENPECKED AS HIS MASTER.

DAME VAN WINKLE REGARDED THEM AS COMPANIONS IN IDLENESS, AND EVEN LOOKED UPON WOLF WITH AN EVIL EYE, AS THE CAUSE OF HIS MASTER'S GOING SO OFTEN ASTRAY.

TIMES GREW WORSE AND WORSE WITH RIP VAN WINKLE AS YEARS OF MATRIMONY ROLLED ON...

...FOR A TART TEMPER NEVER MELLOWS WITH AGE...

...AND A SHARP TONGUE IS THE ONLY EDGED TOOL THAT GROWS KEENER WITH CONSTANT USE.

FOR A LONG WHILE HE USED TO CONSOLE HIMSELF, WHEN DRIVEN FROM HOME, BY FREQUENTING A KIND OF PERPETUAL CLUB OF THE SAGES, PHILOSOPHERS, AND OTHER IDLE PERSONAGES OF THE VILLAGE, WHICH HELD ITS SESSIONS ON A BENCH BEFORE A SMALL INN.

HERE THEY USED TO SIT IN THE SHADE THROUGH A LONG, LAZY SUMMER'S DAY, TALKING LISTLESSLY OVER VILLAGE GOSSIP, OR TELLING ENDLESS SLEEPY STORIES ABOUT NOTHING.

BUT FROM EVEN THIS STRONGHOLD THE UNLUCKY RIP WAS AT LENGTH ROUTED BY HIS WIFE, WHO WOULD SUDDENLY BREAK IN UPON THE TRANQUILITY OF THE ASSEMBLAGE AND CALL THE MEMBERS ALL TO NAUGHT.

POOR RIP WAS AT LAST REDUCED ALMOST TO DESPAIR.

HIS ONLY ALTERNATIVE, TO ESCAPE FROM THE LABOR OF THE FARM AND CLAMOR OF HIS WIFE, WAS TO TAKE GUN IN HAND AND STROLL AWAY INTO THE WOODS.

HERE HE WOULD SOMETIMES SEAT HIMSELF AT THE FOOT OF A TREE AND SHARE THE CONTENTS OF HIS WALLET WITH WOLF.

POOR WOLF, THY MISTRESS LEADS THEE A DOG'S LIFE OF IT; BUT NEVER MIND, MY LAD, WHILST I LIVE THOU SHALT NEVER WANT A FRIEND TO STAND BY THEE!

IF DOGS CAN FEEL PITY, I VERILY BELIEVE HE RECIPROCATED THE SENTIMENT WITH ALL HIS HEART.

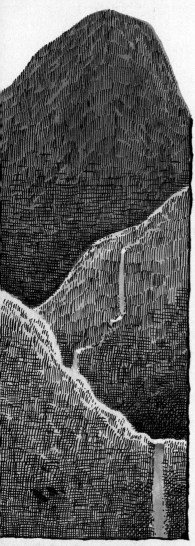

IN A LONG RAMBLE OF THE KIND ON A FINE AUTUMNAL DAY RIP HAD UNCONSCIOUSLY SCRAMBLED TO ONE OF THE HIGHEST PARTS OF THE KAATSKILL MOUNTAINS.

HE WAS AFTER HIS FAVORITE SPORT OF SQUIRREL HUNTING...

...AND THE STILL SOLITUDES HAD ECHOED AND REECHOED WITH THE REPORTS OF HIS GUN.

HE LOOKED DOWN INTO A DEEP MOUNTAIN GLEN, WILD, LONELY AND SHAGGED, THE BOTTOM FILLED WITH FRAGMENTS FROM THE IMPENDING CLIFFS AND SCARELY LIGHTED BY THE REFLECTED RAYS OF THE SETTING SUN.

IT WOULD BE DARK LONG BEFORE HE REACHED THE VILLAGE, AND HE HEAVED A HEAVY SIGH WHEN HE THOUGHT OF ENCOUNTERING THE TERRORS OF DAME VAN WINKLE.

AS HE WAS ABOUT TO DESCEND...

RIP VAN WINKLE! RIP VAN WINKLE!

HE LOOKED AROUND BUT COULD SEE NOTHING.

HE THOUGHT HIS FANCY MUST HAVE DECEIVED HIM AND TURNED AGAIN TO DESCEND, WHEN HE HEARD THE SAME CRY...

RIP VAN WINKLE! RIP VAN WINKLE!

HE PERCEIVED A STRANGE FIGURE SLOWLY TOILING UP THE ROCKS...

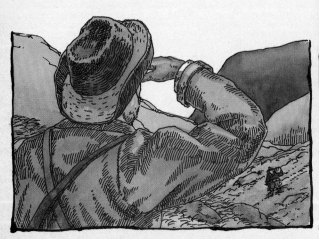

HE WAS SURPRISED TO SEE ANY HUMAN BEING IN THIS LONELY AND UNFREQUENTED PLACE.

BUT SUPPOSING IT TO BE A NEIGHBOR IN NEED OF HIS ASSISTANCE, HE HASTENED DOWN TO YIELD TO IT.

ON NEARER APPROACH, HE WAS STILL MORE SURPRISED AT THE SINGULARITY OF THE STRANGER'S APPEARANCE.

HE BORE ON HIS SHOULDER A STOUT KEG, AND MADE SIGNS FOR RIP TO APPROACH AND ASSIST HIM WITH THE LOAD.

THOUGH RATHER SHY AND DISTRUSTFUL OF THIS NEW ACQUAINTANCE, RIP COMPLIED WITH HIS USUAL EAGERNESS.

As they ascended, Rip every now and then heard long, rolling peals, like distant thunder, that seemed to issue out of a deep ravine toward which their rugged path conducted.

HE PAUSED FOR AN INSTANT...

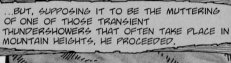

...BUT, SUPPOSING IT TO BE THE MUTTERING OF ONE OF THOSE TRANSIENT THUNDERSHOWERS THAT OFTEN TAKE PLACE IN MOUNTAIN HEIGHTS, HE PROCEEDED.

ON ENTERING THE AMPHITHEATER, NEW OBJECTS OF WONDER PRESENTED THEMSELVES.

WHAT SEEMED PARTICULARLY ODD TO RIP WAS THAT, THOUGH THESE FOLKS WERE EVIDENTLY AMUSING THEMSELVES, THEY MAINTAINED THE GRAVEST FACES, THE MOST MYSTERIOUS SILENCE, AND WERE THUS THE MOST MELANCHOLY PARTY OF PLEASURE HE HAD EVER WITNESSED.

NOTHING INTERRUPTED THE STILLNESS OF THE SCENE BUT THE NOISE OF THE BALLS, WHICH, WHENEVER THEY WERE ROLLED, ECHOED ALONG THE MOUNTAINS LIKE RUMBLING PEALS OF THUNDER.

As Rip and his companion approached them, they suddenly desisted from their play and stared at him with such a fixed, statuelike gaze that his heart turned within him.

His companion now emptied the contents of the keg into large flagons...

...and made signs to him to wait upon the company.

They quaffed the liquor in profound silence and then returned to their game.

By Degrees, Rip's awe and apprehension subsided.

H e even ventured, when no eye was fixed upon him, to taste the beverage.

He was naturally a thirsty soul.

H e reiterated his visits to the flagon so often that at length his senses were overpowered, his eyes swam in his head, his head gradually declined, and he fell into a deep sleep.

SURELY, I HAVE NOT SLEPT HERE ALL NIGHT!

OH! THAT FLAGON! THAT *WICKED* FLAGON! WHAT EXCUSE SHALL I MAKE TO DAME VAN WINKLE?!

HE RECALLED THE OCCURRENCES BEFORE HE FELL ASLEEP...

RIP LOOKED AROUND FOR HIS GUN...

...BUT FOUND ONLY AN OLD FIRELOCK, THE BARREL ENCRUSTED WITH RUST, AND THE STOCK WORM-EATEN.

HE NOW SUSPECTED THAT THE GRAVE ROISTERERS OF THE MOUNTAIN HAD PLAYED A TRICK UPON HIM AND, HAVING DOSED HIM WITH LIQUOR, HAD ROBBED HIM OF HIS GUN.

WOLF!

WOLF, TOO, HAD DISAPPEARED, BUT HE MIGHT HAVE STRAYED AWAY AFTER A SQUIRREL OR PARTRIDGE.

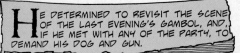

He DETERMINED TO REVISIT THE SCENE OF THE LAST EVENING'S GAMBOL, AND, IF HE MET WITH ANY OF THE PARTY, TO DEMAND HIS DOG AND GUN.

THESE MOUNTAIN BEDS DO NOT AGREE WITH ME!

IF THIS FROLIC SHOULD LAY ME UP WITH A FIT OF RHEUMATISM, I SHALL HAVE A BLESSED TIME WITH DAME VAN WINKLE!

WITH SOME DIFFICULTY HE GOT DOWN INTO THE GLEN.

He FOUND THE GULLY UP WHICH HE AND HIS COMPANION HAD ASCENDED THE PRECEDING EVENING--BUT TO HIS ASTONISHMENT A MOUNTAIN STREAM WAS NOW FOAMING DOWN IT, FILLING THE GLEN WITH BABBLING MURMURS.

At length, he reached to where the ravine had opened through the cliffs to the amphitheater, but no traces of such opening remained.

What was to be done? The morning was passing away, and Rip felt famished for want of his breakfast.

He grieved to give up his dog and gun. He dreaded to meet his wife. But it would not do to starve among the mountains.

He shook his head, shouldered the rusty firelock, and, with a heart full of trouble and anxiety, turned his steps homeward.

AS HE APPROACHED THE VILLAGE HE MET A NUMBER OF PEOPLE, BUT NONE WHOM HE KNEW. THIS SURPRISED HIM SOMEWHAT, FOR HE HAD THOUGHT HIMSELF ACQUAINTED WITH EVERYONE AROUND THE COUNTRYSIDE.

THEIR DRESS, TOO, WAS OF A DIFFERENT FASHION FROM THAT TO WHICH HE WAS ACCUSTOMED.

TO HIS ASTONISHMENT, HE FOUND HIS BEARD HAD GROWN A FOOT LONG!

THEY ALL STARED AT HIM WITH EQUAL MARKS OF SURPRISE, AND WHENEVER THEY CAST THEIR EYES UPON HIM, THEY INVARIABLY STROKED THEIR CHINS. THE CONSTANT RECURRANCE OF THIS GESTURE INDUCED RIP, INVOLUNTARILY, TO DO THE SAME.

A TROOP OF STRANGE CHILDREN NOW RAN AT HIS HEELS, HOOTING AFTER HIM AND POINTING AT HIS GREY BEARD. THE DOGS, TOO, NOT ONE OF WHICH HE RECOGNIZED, BARKED AT HIM AS HE PASSED.

THERE WERE ROWS OF HOUSES THAT HE HAD NEVER SEEN BEFORE, AND THOSE THAT HAD BEEN HIS FAMILIAR HAUNTS HAD DISAPPEARED. STRANGE NAMES WERE OVER THE DOORS--STRANGE FACES AT THE WINDOWS. EVERYTHING WAS STRANGE.

THAT FLAGON LAST NIGHT HAS ADDLED MY POOR HEAD SADLY.

HIS MIND NOW MISGAVE HIM. HE BEGAN TO DOUBT WHETHER BOTH HE AND THE WORLD AROUND HIM WERE NOT BEWITCHED. RIP WAS SORELY PERPLEXED.

IT WAS WITH SOME DIFFICULTY THAT HE FOUND THE WAY TO HIS OWN HOUSE, WHICH HE APPROACHED WITH SILENT AWE, EXPECTING EVERY MOMENT TO HEAR THE SHRILL VOICE OF DAME VAN WINKLE.

HE FOUND THE HOUSE HAD GONE TO DECAY--THE ROOF FALLEN IN, THE WINDOWS SHATTERED, AND THE DOORS OFF THE HINGES.

A HALF-STARVED DOG THAT LOOKED LIKE WOLF WAS SKULKING ABOUT. RIP CALLED HIM BY NAME, BUT THE CUR SNARLED, SHOWED HIS TEETH, AND PASSED ON.

HE ENTERED THE HOUSE, WHICH DAME VAN WINKLE HAD ALWAYS KEPT IN NEAT ORDER.

IT WAS EMPTY, FORLORN AND APPARENTLY ABANDONED. THIS DESOLATENESS OVERCAME ALL HIS CONNUBIAL FEARS. HE CALLED LOUDLY FOR HIS WIFE AND CHILDREN. THE LONELY CHAMBERS RANG FOR A MOMENT WITH HIS VOICE, AND THEN ALL AGAIN WAS SILENCE.

He now hurried forth and hastened to his old resort, the village inn, but it, too, was gone. A large, rickety, wooden building stood in its place. A strange flag fluttered in the breeze. A picture Rip at first took to be of King George bore the unfamiliar name of a general.

...THE HEROES OF SEVENTY-SIX!

HE LOOKED IN VAIN FOR NICOLAS VEDDER OR VAN BUMMEL, THE SCHOOLMASTER.

VOTE Bummel CONGRESS

Vote Zanden —for— Congress

THERE WAS, AS USUAL, A CROWD ABOUT THE INN, BUT NONE THAT RIP RECOLLECTED. THE VERY CHARACTER OF THE PEOPLE HAD CHANGED, AND THEY SPOKE OF ELECTIONS-- CONGRESS--BUNKER HILL--AND OTHER WORDS WHICH WERE A PERFECT BABYLONIAN JARGON TO THE BEWILDERED RIP VAN WINKLE.

A TORY!!

A SPY!!

AWAY WITH HIM!

PLEASE...I MEAN NO HARM. I CAME IN SEARCH OF MY NEIGHBORS.

WELL... WHO ARE THEY? NAME THEM.

WHERE'S NICHOLAS VEDDER?

NICHOLAS VEDDER! WHY...HE IS DEAD AND GONE THESE EIGHTEEN YEARS!

BROM DUTCHER?

HE WENT OFF TO THE ARMY IN THE BEGINNING OF THE WAR. HE NEVER CAME BACK AGAIN.

WHERE'S VAN BUMMEL, THE SCHOOLMASTER?

HE WENT OFF TO THE WARS, TOO, AND IS NOW IN CONGRESS.

RIP'S HEART DIED AWAY AT HEARING OF THESE SAD CHANGES IN HIS HOME AND FRIENDS, AND FINDING HIMSELF THUS ALONE IN THE WORLD.

HE HAD NO COURAGE TO ASK AFTER MORE FRIENDS, BUT CRIED OUT IN DESPAIR.

DOES NOBODY HERE KNOW RIP VAN WINKLE?

RIP...

...VAN WINKLE?

TO BE SURE! THAT'S RIP VAN WINKLE YONDER, LEANING AGAINST THE TREE.

RIP LOOKED AND BEHELD A PRECISE COUNTERPART OF HIMSELF AS HE WENT UP THE MOUNTAIN, APPARENTLY AS LAZY AND CERTAINLY AS RAGGED. THE POOR FELLOW WAS NOW COMPLETELY CONFOUNDED.

GOD KNOWS, I'M NOT MYSELF--I'M SOMEBODY ELSE. THAT'S ME YONDER...NO, THAT'S SOMEBODY ELSE GOT INTO MY SHOES. I WAS MYSELF LAST NIGHT, BUT I FELL ASLEEP ON THE MOUNTAIN, AND THEY'VE CHANGED MY GUN, AND EVERYTHING'S CHANGED, AND I'M CHANGED, AND I CAN'T TELL WHAT'S MY NAME, OR WHO I AM!

AT THIS CRITICAL MOMENT, A FRESH, COMELY WOMAN PRESSED THROUGH THE THRONG TO GET A PEEP AT THE GREY-BEARDED MAN. SHE HAD A CHUBBY CHILD IN HER ARMS WHICH, FRIGHTENED AT HIS LOOKS, BEGAN TO CRY.

HUSH, RIP, HUSH. THE OLD MAN WON'T HURT YOU.

WHAT, MY GOOD WOMAN, IS YOUR NAME?

JUDITH GARDENIER.

AND YOUR FATHER'S NAME?

AH, POOR MAN. RIP VAN WINKLE WAS HIS NAME. BUT IT'S TWENTY YEARS SINCE HE WENT AWAY FROM HOME. HE NEVER HAS BEEN HEARD OF SINCE. WHETHER HE SHOT HIMSELF OR WAS CARRIED AWAY BY THE INDIANS, NOBODY CAN TELL. I WAS THEN BUT A LITTLE GIRL.

RIP HAD BUT ONE QUESTION MORE TO ASK, AND HE PUT IT WITH A FALTERING VOICE:

WHERE'S YOUR MOTHER?

SHE, TOO, DIED BUT A SHORT TIME SINCE. SHE BROKE A BLOOD VESSEL IN A FIT OF PASSION AT A NEW ENGLAND PEDDLER.

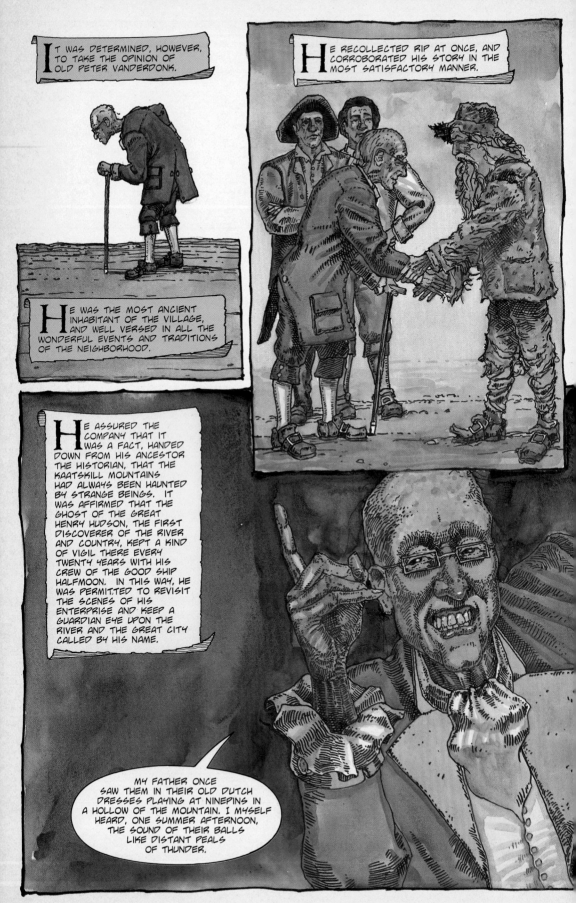

IT WAS DETERMINED, HOWEVER, TO TAKE THE OPINION OF OLD PETER VANDERDONK.

HE RECOLLECTED RIP AT ONCE, AND CORROBORATED HIS STORY IN THE MOST SATISFACTORY MANNER.

HE WAS THE MOST ANCIENT INHABITANT OF THE VILLAGE, AND WELL VERSED IN ALL THE WONDERFUL EVENTS AND TRADITIONS OF THE NEIGHBORHOOD.

HE ASSURED THE COMPANY THAT IT WAS A FACT, HANDED DOWN FROM HIS ANCESTOR THE HISTORIAN, THAT THE KAATSKILL MOUNTAINS HAD ALWAYS BEEN HAUNTED BY STRANGE BEINGS. IT WAS AFFIRMED THAT THE GHOST OF THE GREAT HENRY HUDSON, THE FIRST DISCOVERER OF THE RIVER AND COUNTRY, KEPT A KIND OF VIGIL THERE EVERY TWENTY YEARS WITH HIS CREW OF THE GOOD SHIP HALFMOON. IN THIS WAY, HE WAS PERMITTED TO REVISIT THE SCENES OF HIS ENTERPRISE AND KEEP A GUARDIAN EYE UPON THE RIVER AND THE GREAT CITY CALLED BY HIS NAME.

MY FATHER ONCE SAW THEM IN THEIR OLD DUTCH DRESSES PLAYING AT NINEPINS IN A HOLLOW OF THE MOUNTAIN. I MYSELF HEARD, ONE SUMMER AFTERNOON, THE SOUND OF THEIR BALLS LIKE DISTANT PEALS OF THUNDER.

40

To make a long story short, the company broke up and returned to the more important concerns of the election.

Rip's daughter took him home to live with her. She had a snug, well-furnished house and a stout, cheery farmer for a husband--whom Rip recollected as one of the urchins that used to climb his back.

As to Rip's son and heir, who was the ditto of himself, seen leaning against the tree, he was employed to work on the farm. But he evinced an hereditary disposition to attend to anything else but his business.

RIP NOW RESUMED HIS OLD WALKS AND HABITS. HE SOON FOUND MANY OF HIS FORMER CRONIES, THOUGH ALL RATHER WORSE FOR THE WEAR AND TEAR OF TIME.

THERE, HE PREFERRED MAKING FRIENDS AMONG THE RISING GENERATION WITH WHOM HE SOON GREW INTO GREAT FAVOR.

RIP TOOK HIS PLACE ONCE MORE ON THE BENCH AT THE INN DOOR AND WAS REVERENCED AS ONE OF THE PATRIARCHS OF THE VILLAGE AND A CHRONICLE OF THE OLD TIMES "BEFORE THE WAR."

IT WAS SOME TIME BEFORE HE COULD GET INTO THE REGULAR TRACK OF GOSSIP OR COULD BE MADE TO COMPREHEND THE STRANGE EVENTS THAT HAD TAKEN PLACE DURING HIS TORPOR--THAT THERE HAD BEEN A REVOLUTIONARY WAR, THAT THE COUNTRY HAD THROWN OFF THE YOKE OF OLD ENGLAND, AND THAT HE WAS NOW A FREE CITIZEN OF THE UNITED STATES.

HE USED TO TELL HIS STORY TO EVERY STRANGER WHO ARRIVED AT MISTER DOOLITTLE'S HOTEL. HE WAS OBSERVED, AT FIRST, TO VARY ON SOME POINTS EVERY TIME HE TOLD IT, WHICH WAS, DOUBTLESS, OWING TO HIS HAVING SO RECENTLY AWAKENED.

IT AT LAST SETTLED DOWN PRECISELY TO THE TALE I HAVE RELATED, AND EVERY MAN, WOMAN, AND CHILD IN THE NEIGHBORHOOD KNEW IT BY HEART.

SOME ALWAYS PRETENDED TO DOUBT THE REALITY OF IT AND INSISTED THAT RIP HAD BEEN OUT OF HIS HEAD, AND THAT THIS WAS ONE POINT ON WHICH HE ALWAYS REMAINED FLIGHTY.

THE OLD DUTCH INHABITANTS, HOWEVER, ALMOST UNIVERSALLY GAVE IT FULL CREDIT...

EVEN TO THIS DAY, THEY NEVER HEAR A THUNDERSTORM OF A SUMMER AFTERNOON ABOUT THE KAATSKILLS BUT THEY SAY HENRY HUDSON AND HIS CREW ARE BUSY AT THEIR GAME OF NINEPINS.

AND IT WAS A COMMON WISH OF ALL HENPECKED HUSBANDS IN THE NEIGHBORHOOD, WHEN LIFE HANGS HEAVY ON THEIR HANDS, THAT THEY MIGHT MOMENTARILY PUT ASIDE WOE AND HAVE A QUIETING DRAFT OUT OF RIP VAN WINKLE'S FLAGON.

Washington Irving was born in New York City in 1783, the youngest of eleven children of a wealthy merchant. A frail and delicate youth, Irving was educated to practice law, but his indulgent family allowed him to lead the leisurely life of a man of letters. Irving's first publication was a series of humorous sketches written for his brothers' newspapers under the pen name of Jonathon Oldstyle, Gent. To restore his fragile health and further his education, Irving traveled in Europe (1804-06), where he gathered material later used in his stories and essays. In 1807, he collaborated with his brother, William, and another writer on *Salmagundi; or the Whim-Whams and Opinions of Launcelot Lanstaff, Esq., and Others.* This collection of satirical pieces about New York society brought Irving instant local renown. His first solo book, *A History of New York from the Beginning of the World to the End of the Dutch Dynasty* (1809), a burlesque by the pseudonymous Dutch-American scholar Diedrich Knickerbocker, broadened Irving's following. His success, though, was marred by tragedy when his fiancée suddenly died. During the next six years, Irving forsook writing; he immersed himself in the family business, busied himself with a number of publishing projects, and, in the War of 1812, served as aide-de-camp to the governor of New York. In 1815, he sailed to Liverpool, England, to oversee the family business there. Three years later, the business failed, and Irving was forced to write for a living. Constantly searching for material, he traveled widely, spending time in England, France, Spain, and Germany. His best-known work, *The Sketch Book of Geoffrey Crayon, Gent.,* appeared in 1820; among the contents were Americanized versions of a number of European folk tales, including *Rip Van Winkle* and *The Legend of Sleepy Hollow.* The Sketch Book was followed by *Bracebridge Hall* (1822), and *Tales of a Traveller* (1824). The latter was so poorly received that Irving was briefly discouraged from writing. He became a U.S. diplomatic attaché in Spain (1826-1829), a setting that inspired his *History of the Life and Voyages of Columbus* (1828), *The Conquest of Granada* (1829), *Companions of Columbus* (1831), and *The Legends of the Alhambra* (1832). In 1832, after serving briefly at the U.S. embassy in London, Irving returned to New York and was warmly welcomed as the first American author to achieve international acclaim. A trip across the American western frontier resulted in *A Tour on the Prairies* (1835), *Astoria* (1836), and *The Adventures of Captain Bonneville* (1837). After a few years in America, during which he declined the nomination for mayor of New York and the secretaryship of the Navy, Irving returned in 1842 to Spain, where he served as U.S. minister. He resigned after two years, spent a year in London on a diplomatic mission, and then returned to the United States for good, settling in at his home in Tarrytown, New York. During his final years, Irving produced two books of sketches, *A Book of the Hudson* (1849) and *Wolfert's Roost* (1855), and several biographies, including the monumental, five-volume *Life of Washington* (1855-59). Irving died in 1859.

Jeffrey Busch was born in Chicago in 1962, and attended the American Academy of Art. He spent eight years in advertising, before turning to the illustration of children's books and magazine covers. *Rip Van Winkle* is his debut in the comics field.